Longman Practice Exam Papers

GCSE Chemistry

John Sadler

Series editors:

Geoff Black and Stuart Wall

Titles available for GCSE

Biology

Chemistry

Mathematics (Intermediate)

Mathematics (Higher)

Physics

Science

Addison Wesley Longman Ltd,
Edinburgh Gate, Harlow,
CM20 2JE, England
and Associated Companies throughout the World

First Published 1998

ISBN 0 582 35645 8

British Library Cataloguing-in-Publication Data
A catalogue record for this book is available from the British Library.

Set in Times 11/13pt by 38

ted in Great Britain by Henry Ling Ltd at The Dorset Press, Dorchester, Dorset.

Contents

Editors' Preface

Longman Practice Exam Papers are written by experienced GCSE examiners and teachers. They will provide you with an ideal opportunity to practise under exam-type conditions before your actual school or college mocks or before the GCSE examination itself. As well as becoming familiar with the vital skill of pacing yourself through a whole exam paper, you can check your answers against examiner solutions and mark-schemes to assess the level you have reached.

Longman Practice Exam Papers can be used alongside the *Longman GCSE Study Guides* and *Longman Exam Practice Kits* to provide a comprehensive range of home study support as you prepare to take your GCSE in each subject covered.

Acknowledgements

I am very grateful for the help of the staff at Addison Wesley Longman, in particular Bridget Allen and Linda Marsh who have worked wonders in getting this book together under a most taxing timetable.

I would like to thank Peter Radford, with whom I worked for many years as a co-Chief Examiner for Chemistry for one of the major examining boards, for agreeing to look through the questions for me. His advice and help were gratefully received.

Finally, I must thank my wife who puts up with the many evenings I spend in my study writing – but she manages to feed and water me on time and still keeps smiling.

JOHN SADLER

How to use this book

- This book is designed to help you to prepare for your GCSE examination. The questions are set at the same standard as the GCSE examination. The aim is to ensure that you attain the highest level that you can get. By using this book carefully and sensibly you will be able to use the information supplied by the author to improve your grades and ensure success.

- Try to take the tests under GCSE conditions. A quiet room, plus all the necessary equipment and a clock is ideal. Use the marking scheme to check your performance.

- Remember that the paper will include a copy of the Periodic Table, so you do not have to learn every element and its symbol.

- The Foundation Tier papers are aimed at students who are expected to get grades C to G; the Higher Tier papers are for students expected to get grades A* to D. Do not despair if you cannot do the Higher papers – the examination is trying to find out what you know, understand and can do. This should be your attitude too; that you will show the examiner what you can do. Remember this – examiners are trying to find out what you know, hence only questions that are on your syllabus are set.

- Read the questions at least twice and underline key words. You will score no marks unless you answer the questions asked.

- You may find some questions more difficult to answer than others, do not be put off by this. Try your best to answer the question – you may find that you score some marks.

- Always make sure that your answers are concise and relevant.

- Make sure you keep an eye on the clock and check your progress every 15 minutes. Do not spend all your time trying to answer one question – you must try to attempt them all. If you get stuck on a question, leave it and come back to it later.

- If you manage to finish early, go back and check your work. Do NOT make any changes unless you are certain that you have made a mistake. Your first instinct as to the correct answer is usually the right one.

- The number of lines under each sub-question indicates how many details are required, as does the mark for each section. If there are three marks available for a question then you must make sure that you have at least three separate points in your answer.

- If the question involves you having to solve a problem make sure that you show all your working. There are marks for the method you adopt as well as for the correct answer with the correct units.

- Make sure that you have all the necessary equipment – calculator (preferably with new batteries), pencils, pens, rubber, ruler.

- Make sure any diagrams are neatly drawn and clearly labelled.

- Most important, be positive – it is never too early to start revision. If you feel you have under-performed in any of these test papers, spend time revising that particular topic and try the test again.

- There are answers and tips for each of the question papers. If you are not sure that your answer is correct, ask your teacher or another responsible person – do not be too over-generous with yourself – it might give you undue expectations.

- Make sure that you have answered ALL the questions – even if you think you do not know the answer, guess. You cannot lose marks!

Using these practice exam papers

In this book there are two Foundation papers and two Higher papers, made up as follows:

Paper	Time (mins)	Marks
Foundation 1	90	100
Foundation 2	60	60
Higher 1	90	100
Higher 2	60	60

The answers and mark-schemes to these papers are given at the end of the papers. Use these to check your answers **after** you have attempted to answer the questions to the best of your ability. Try to answer all the questions – do not give up too easily.

Attempt the Foundation Tier papers first – if you score more than 120 marks you should attempt the Higher Tier papers – if less than 120 marks you will need to do more revision.

Longman Examination Board

General Certificate of Secondary Education

Chemistry

Foundation Paper 1

Time: 90 minutes

Instructions

- Answer **all** the questions.
- Write your answers in the spaces provided.
- Use a blue or black ink or ball-point pen.
- Show all stages in any calculations and state the units.

Information for candidates

- The number of marks is given in brackets at the end of each question or part-question. The total mark for the question is given at the end of the question.
- Marks will **not** be deducted for wrong answers.
- The Periodic Table is printed on page 52.
- This paper has 8 questions.
- The maximum mark for this paper is 100.

Number	Mark
1.	
2.	
3.	
4.	
5.	
6.	
7.	
8.	

1. The key shown below can be used to work out if metal compounds are soluble or insoluble in water.

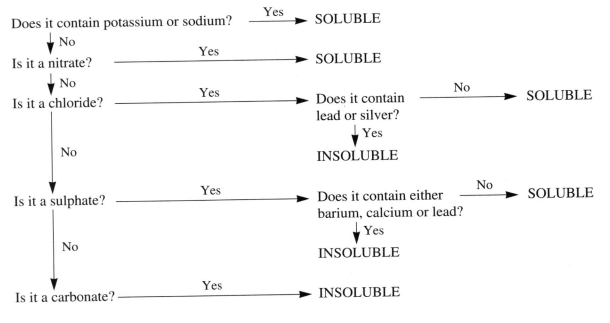

Leave margin blank

Turn over

3

Complete the following table by placing a ✓ in the appropriate column.

Compound	Soluble	Insoluble
sodium carbonate	✓	
aluminium nitrate		
barium chloride		
zinc sulphate		
lead carbonate		

Total: 4 marks

2. Use the Periodic Table which is printed on page 52 to answer the questions below.

(a) Complete the following table which refers to one atom of argon, $^{40}_{18}$ Ar.

number of protons	
number of electrons	
number of neutrons	

(3 marks)

(b) (i) Which element has 1 more proton than argon?

....

(ii) In which group of the Periodic Table is the element you have named in (b)(i)?

....

(iii) Which element has the same atomic mass as argon?

....

(iv) In which group of the Periodic Table is the element you have named in (b)(iii)?

....

(4 marks)

(c) An element in the same period as argon reacts with steam, but only very slowly with cold water. When the element reacts with steam the products are a colourless gas and a white solid. Name:

(i) the element   ....

(ii) the colourless gas   ....

(iii) the white solid   ....

(3 marks)

(d) About 1% of the atmosphere is argon.

(i) What is the commonest gas in the air?   ....

(ii) What percentage of the air is this gas?   ....

(2 marks)

(e) Give one use of argon.

....

(1 mark)

(f) (i) Why is helium preferred to hydrogen in balloons?

....

(ii) Suggest why krypton, which is in the same group as argon and helium, is not used in balloons.

....

(2 marks)

Total: 15 marks

3. The apparatus shown below was used for the following two experiments:

Experiment 1 To find the percentage of oxygen in air.

Experiment 2 To study the decomposition of ammonia.

In each experiment iron wool was put into the hard glass tube.

Results for experiment 1
100 cm^3 of air was passed over the heated iron wool. The wool glowed red hot and when the apparatus was left to cool to room temperature, 80 cm^3 of gas remained.

(a) What gas is removed by the iron wool? ....

(1 mark)

(b) How does the mass of the hard glass tube and its contents change during this experiment?

....

(1 mark)

(c) What is the percentage of oxygen in air?

....

(1 mark)

(d) How would the results have differed if 100 cm^3 of exhaled air had been used, and why?

....

(2 marks)

Results for experiment 2
The apparatus was set up again. All the air was removed from the apparatus and it was gently warmed to make sure that it was completely dry. 40 cm^3 of ammonia was put into the apparatus and passed over the heated iron wool. When the apparatus was left to cool to room temperature, 80 cm^3 of gas remained.

Turn over

(e) Suggest a gas that could be used to remove all the air from the apparatus. The gas used must not react with iron wool.

....

(1 mark)

(f) Why is it important that the apparatus is dry?

....

(2 marks)

(g) The products of the reaction were nitrogen and hydrogen only. What does this tell you about the composition of ammonia?

....

(1 mark)

(h) The mass of the hard glass tube and its contents did not change during this experiment. What is the purpose of using iron wool in this experiment?

....

(1 mark)

(i) Ammonia does not burn in air. Would you expect the products formed after passing over iron wool to burn? Explain your answer.

....

....

(2 marks)

Total: 12 marks

4. Barium is in Group 2 of the Periodic Table.

(a) Would you expect it to be more, or less, reactive than magnesium? Explain your answer.

....

....

(2 marks)

(b) Barium is stored in the same way as sodium.

(i) How is barium stored? ....

(ii) What does this tell you about barium?

....

(2 marks)

(c) Describe what you would expect to observe if you passed carbon dioxide into barium hydroxide solution until no further changes took place.

....

....

(2 marks)

(d) Either barium chloride or barium nitrate is used to test for the sulphate ion. Before adding either of these chemicals, dilute hydrochloric acid or dilute nitric acid is added to prevent barium carbonate from being formed. Explain how the addition of one of these acids prevents the formation of barium carbonate.

....

....

(2 marks)

Total: 8 marks

5. This question is about the chemistry of iron and aluminium and their compounds.
   (a) Where would you find (i) aluminium and (ii) iron in the Periodic Table?

   (i) aluminium ....

   (ii) iron ....

   (2 marks)

   (b) Apart from its use as a catalyst, give two other typical properties of iron that can be deduced from its position in the Periodic Table.

   1. ....

   2. ....

   (2 marks)

   (c) Explain why, although aluminium is more reactive than iron, aluminium reacts slowly with dilute hydrochloric acid whereas iron reacts very rapidly.

   ....

   ....

   (2 marks)

   (d) Complete the following table that compares iron(III) oxide and aluminium oxide

	aluminium oxide	iron(III) oxide
formula of oxide		Fe_2O_3
name of ore containing oxide		haematite
method of extracting metal from its ore	electrolysis	
use of metal	manufacture of pots and pans	
reaction of oxide with dilute hydrochloric acid	reacts to give a colourless solution	
reaction with sodium hydroxide		no reaction
use as a catalyst	converting ethanol to ethene	

(7 marks)

Turn over

(e) What is meant by an *ore*?

....

....

(2 marks)

(f) Suggest a reason for each of the following:

  (i) why most car bodies are made from steel and not aluminium

....

  (ii) why the centres of electricity cables are aluminium and not iron

....

(2 marks)

(g) Rust is hydrated iron(III) oxide. Describe an experiment to show that rust contains water.

....

....

....

(3 marks)

Total: 20 marks

6. The key below can be used to identify some common rocks:

Does it react with hydrochloric acid?

Yes → **marble or limestone**   No → **slate or sandstone or granite**

does it contain fossils?   does it split into layers?

Yes → **limestone**   No → **marble**   Yes → **slate**   No → **sandstone or granite**

(a) What gas is given off when hydrochloric acid reacts with marble or limestone?

....

(1 mark)

(b) Continue the above key to show how you distinguish between sandstone and granite.

(2 marks)

Leave margin blank

(c) Divide the rocks into the three types; igneous, metamorphic and sedimentary, and complete the table below

igneous	metamorphic	sedimentary

(3 marks)

(d) Explain why metamorphic rocks are found in ancient mountain ranges.

....

....

(2 marks)

(e) (i) Give two pieces of evidence that suggest that South America and Africa were part of the same land mass called the Pangaea.

....

....

(ii) What name is given to the process of the break-up and separation of the Pangaea into several large land masses?

....

(3 marks)

Total: 11 marks

7. Dalton (1766–1844) proposed various symbols for different 'elements'.

A few are listed below.

alumina   carbon   hydrogen   nitrogen   oxygen

(a) Explain why

(i) Dalton did not have any symbols for the rare (noble) gases – Group 0

....

(ii) Dalton thought that alumina (aluminium oxide) was an element

....

(2 marks)

Turn over

Using Dalton's symbols, different substances can be drawn.

ammonia carbon dioxide ethene hydrogen oxygen water
A   B   C   D   E   F

(b) Using the letters A, B, C, D, E and F choose from these substances:

(i) a substance that is a liquid at room temperature and pressure ....

(ii) substances that have molecules that are diatomic ....

(iii) substances that are compounds ....

(iv) a substance that is obtained by the fractional distillation of liquid air ....

(v) an organic substance that can be obtained by cracking octane (C_8H_{18}) ....

(7 marks)

(c) Write down, using modern-day chemical symbols, the formula for substance A.

....

(1 mark)

(d) For substance C write down its:

(i) molecular formula ....

(ii) its empirical formula ....

(2 marks)

(e) How would you recognise substance A from the following tests? (Describe each test and give the result.)

(i) a physical property

....

(ii) using moist litmus paper

....

(2 marks)

Total: 14 marks

8. Copper can be obtained from copper(II) oxide by heating the copper(II) oxide with excess magnesium. The reaction is very exothermic.

(a) (i) Which metal is the more reactive, magnesium or copper? Explain your answer.

....

(1 mark)

(ii) What is meant by the term 'exothermic'?

....

(1 mark)

(iii) Complete the word equation

Copper oxide + magnesium → ....

(1 mark)

(iv) Name the **three** substances left in the mixture after excess magnesium has reacted with copper(II) oxide.

.... and .... and ....

(2 marks)

(b) Complete the following descriptions of the appearances of the products and reactants. The first one has been done for you.

copper(II) oxide is a **black solid**

copper is a .... metal

magnesium is a silvery shiny ....

magnesium oxide is a .... solid

(3 marks)

(c) (i) Describe how you would obtain pure, dry copper from the mixture using dilute sulphuric acid. You should use your knowledge of the reactivity series of metals. Magnesium oxide reacts with dilute sulphuric acid to form magnesium sulphate which is very soluble in water. (You may use diagrams in your description.)

....

....

....

....

....

(5 marks)

(ii) How would you show that copper is a metal?

....

(1 mark)

(d) State two uses of copper.

.... and ....

(2 marks)

Total: 16 marks

Longman
Examination Board

General Certificate of Secondary Education
Chemistry
Foundation Paper 2

Time: 60 minutes

Instructions

■ Answer **all** the questions.

■ Write your answers in the spaces provided.

■ Use a blue or black ink or ball-point pen.

■ Show all stages in any calculations and state the units.

Information for candidates

■ The number of marks is given in brackets at the end of each question or part-question. The total mark for the question is given at the end of the question.

■ Marks will **not** be deducted for wrong answers.

■ The Periodic Table is printed on page 52.

■ This paper has 6 questions.

■ The maximum mark for this paper is 60.

Number	Mark
1.	
2.	
3.	
4.	
5.	
6.	

---

1. Experiments were carried out to find the solubility of potassium nitrate in water at various temperatures.

   In one such experiment potassium nitrate was added to 50 grams of water at room temperature (20 °C). The temperature dropped by 5 °C. When the water was restored to room temperature it was found that 15 g of potassium nitrate were required to form a saturated solution.

   (a) What type of energy change occurs when potassium nitrate is added to water?

   ....

   (1 mark)

   (b) What is meant by the term *saturated solution*?

   ....

   ....

   (2 marks)

Leave margin blank

(c) Use the result from the experiment described to complete the solubility curve for potassium nitrate.

(3 marks)

(d) Use your graph to predict the solubility of potassium nitrate in water at 0 °C

....

(1 mark)

(e) (i) What mass of potassium nitrate would be formed if a beaker in which there was 100 g of water containing a saturated solution of potassium nitrate at 50 °C was plunged into a beaker full of ice?

....

(2 marks)

(ii) What difference would be observed if the solution was allowed to cool slowly from 50 °C to 0 °C?

....

(1 mark)

(f) One of the uses of potassium nitrate is as a fertiliser. If too much potassium nitrate is added, the excess runs into rivers and causes *eutrophication.*

What is meant by eutrophication?

....

....

(2 marks)

Total: 12 marks

Turn over

2. The following graphs were obtained when 0.4 g of small calcium metal lumps were added to (i) 100 cm^3 (excess) of water and (ii) 100 cm^3 (excess) of dilute hydrochloric acid. The hydrogen given off was measured at room temperature and pressure.

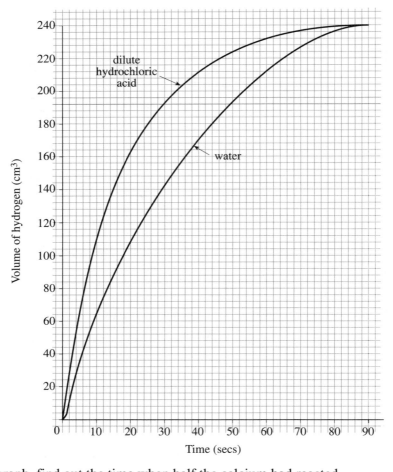

(a) From the graph, find out the time when half the calcium had reacted

    (i) with the water ....

    (ii) with the hydrochloric acid ....

                                                                        (2 marks)

(b) How long did it take for 50 cm^3 of hydrogen to be formed

    (i) with water ....

    (ii) with hydrochloric acid ....

                                                                         (2 marks)

(c) What would be the effect on (i) the rate of reaction and (ii) the total volume of hydrogen formed, if 100 cm^3 of water were added at the start of each experiment

    water experiment   (i) rate ....

                                          (ii) volume of hydrogen ....

    hydrochloric acid experiment   (i) rate ....

                                          (ii) volume of hydrogen ....

                                                                                 (4 marks)

(d) Suggest one way in which the reaction between calcium and water could be speeded up.

....

(1 mark)

Total: 9 marks

3. The water you drink at home and at school has been cleaned and purified. The water has to go through several processes before you can drink it.

(a) What method is used to remove insoluble materials such as stones and wood?

....

(1 mark)

(b) Chlorine is added to water before it leaves the water company.

(i) What is the chemical test for chlorine?

....

....

(2 marks)

(ii) Why is chlorine added to water?

....

(1 mark)

(c) What is the difference between 'permanently hard water' and 'temporarily hard water'?

....

....

(2 marks)

(d) Name a chemical that causes

(i) permanent hardness ....

(ii) temporary hardness ....

(iii) removes both permanent hardness and temporary hardness ....

(3 marks)

(e) Explain how (i) permanent hardness and (ii) temporary hardness get into water.

....

....

....

(3 marks)

Total: 12 marks

Turn over

4. Quicklime is made by heating limestone at about 1000 °C for several hours using a lime kiln.

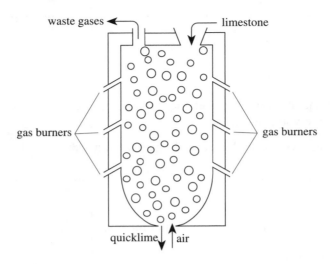

The reaction that takes place is:

$$\text{limestone} \rightarrow \text{quicklime} + \text{carbon dioxide}$$

(a) Give the chemical names for

(i) limestone ....

(ii) quicklime ....

(2 marks)

(b) Explain the presence of the following gases in the waste gases:

(i) carbon dioxide ....

....

(ii) carbon monoxide ....

....

(iii) nitrogen ....

....

(4 marks)

(c) Give a use in each case for:

(i) limestone ....

(ii) quicklime ....

(iii) carbon dioxide ....

(3 marks)

Total: 9 marks

5. The apparatus shown below was used to investigate the action of heat on wood.

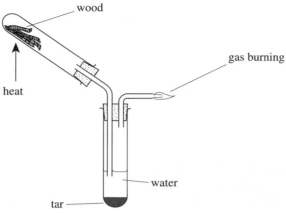

(a) The gas given off burned to form carbon dioxide and water only. What type of organic compound is this gas?

....

(1 mark)

(b) From your answers to (a) suggest two elements that MUST be present in wood.

.... and ....

(2 marks)

(c) The tar collected in the test-tube is a mixture of various organic compounds. Name the process that could be used to separate these compounds.

....

(1 mark)

(d) When universal indicator was added to the aqueous layer at the end of the experiment the pH was 1.

   (i) What is meant by an aqueous solution?

....

   (ii) What does a pH of 1 tell you about this aqueous solution?

....

(2 marks)

(e) Suggest another substance that would give a flammable gas and tar if it were used in this experiment in place of wood.

....

(1 mark)

(f) The product left in the test-tube can be used by artists for drawing pictures and cartoons. Suggest the identity of this substance.

....

(1 mark)

Turn over

(g) Suggest a reason as to why it is necessary to disconnect the apparatus before allowing the test-tube to cool down.

....

....

(2 marks)

Total: 10 marks

6. Read the following statements:

Iron is manufactured by reduction of iron oxide using carbon.
Gold is found in the 'free' state – it occurs naturally.
Sodium can only be manufactured by the electrolysis of molten sodium chloride.

(a) Using this information, place the metals in order of their reactivity.

most reactive   ....

....

least reactive   ....

(2 marks)

(b) Suggest labels for the following diagrams which show an experiment to see if both water and air need to be present in order for iron to rust.

Air present but no water   Water present but no air   Control

(4 marks)

(c) Suggest reasons why

(i) gold is more expensive than an equal mass of sodium

....

(ii) sodium is more expensive than an equal mass of iron

....

(2 marks)

Total: 8 marks

Longman Examination Board

General Certificate of Secondary Education

Chemistry

Higher Paper I

Time: 90 minutes

Instructions

- Answer **all** the questions.

- Write your answers in the spaces provided.

- Use a blue or black ink or ball-point pen.

- Show all stages in any calculations and state the units.

Information for candidates

- The number of marks is given in brackets at the end of each question or part-question. The total mark for the question is given at the end of the question.

- Marks will **not** be deducted for wrong answers.

- The Periodic Table is printed on page 52.

- This paper has 9 questions.

- The maximum mark for this paper is 100.

Number	Mark
1.	
2.	
3.	
4.	
5.	
6.	
7.	
8.	
9.	

1. A black solid, element A, was heated in a beaker of oil as shown in the diagram. When the temperature reached 180 °C the solid A turned directly into a purple gas. The gas was then cooled by a finger condenser, as shown in the diagram, and returned to solid A.

Leave margin blank

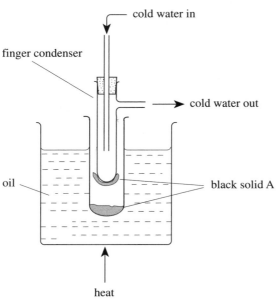

cold water in

finger condenser

cold water out

oil

black solid A

heat

Turn over

(a) Name the process whereby a substance turns directly from a solid to a gas.

.... *evaporation* ....

(1 mark)

(b) Draw a diagram to show the arrangement of particles in solid A and in gas A.

solid A   gas A

(2 marks)

(c) Draw a graph of temperature against time for the action of heat on solid A. Explain the shape of your graph.

(3 marks)

(d) Suggest why oil was used to heat solid A and not water.

.... *because oil will not evaporate when it reaches 100°C* ....

(1 mark)

(e) (i) Solid A is in Group 7 of the Periodic Table. Suggest an identity for A.

.... *Iodine* ....

(ii) What evidence is there to suggest that A is a non-metal?

....

(iii) Name another solid non-metal.

.... *Carbon* ....

(3 marks)

Total: 10 marks

2. The diagram below shows an apparatus for the production and collection of carbon dioxide.

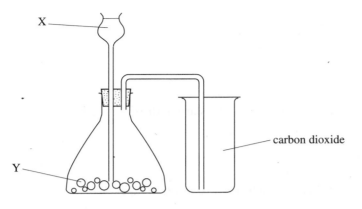

X——

Y——

carbon dioxide

(a) Suggest the identities of X and Y.

X is ....Hydrochloric acid..

Y is ....marble...

(2 marks)

(b) Carbon dioxide is a colourless gas. What other physical property can be deduced from the above method of preparation and collection?

...............It is heavier than air (denser than air.................................

(1 mark)

(c) Carbon dioxide can be formed by a number of different types of reaction. Suggest identities for each of the following:

(i) a liquid that burns to give carbon dioxide and water

....

(ii) a solid that burns to give carbon dioxide only

................carbon...

(iii) a gas that burns to give carbon dioxide only

....

(iv) a solid that when heated gives carbon dioxide as one of the two products

....

(v) a solution of a solid in water that produces carbon dioxide when yeast is added

....

(5 marks)

(d) Using dots and crosses to represent electrons, draw the arrangements of electrons in carbon dioxide.

(2 marks)

Turn over

(e) Carbon and silicon are both in Group 4 of the Periodic Table. Suggest why carbon dioxide is a gas and silicon dioxide is a solid.

....

....

(2 marks)

(f) Name a metal, the manufacture of which produces carbon dioxide as a by-product.

....

(1 mark)

(g) When ammonium carbonate is heated the following reaction takes place:

$$(NH_4)_2CO_3 \ (s) \rightarrow 2NH_3 \ (g) + CO_2 \ (g) + 2H_2O \ (l)$$

Calculate the total volume of gas given off at room temperature and pressure (rtp), when 1 mole of ammonium carbonate is heated.

(1 mole of any gas at rtp occupies 24 litres)

....

....

(2 marks)

Total: 15 marks

3. The apparatus below was set up to study the rate at which oxygen is evolved from a solution of hydrogen peroxide. As soon as the apparatus had been set up a stop clock was started.

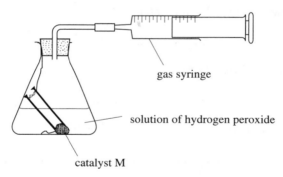

gas syringe

solution of hydrogen peroxide

catalyst M

After a certain length of time, the flask was shaken so that the black powdered catalyst (M) came into contact with the hydrogen peroxide. The graph obtained is shown below.

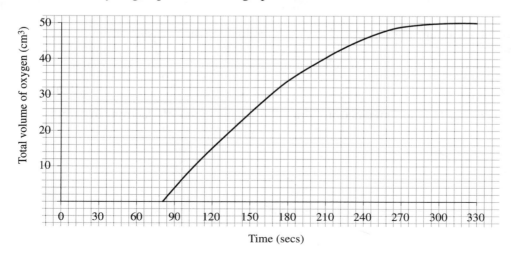

Leave margin blank

(a) What is the test for oxygen?

....

....

(2 marks)

(b) (i) The catalyst M was a metal oxide. Suggest the identity of the catalyst.

....

(ii) Is the metal in the catalyst a Group 1, Group 2, Group 3, or transition metal?

....

(iii) One of the properties of this metal or one of its compounds is that it acts as a catalyst. Give one other property of similar metals or their compounds.

....

(iv) Name a metal that can be used as a catalyst in an industrial process. Name the process which uses the catalyst.

....

(4 marks)

(c) At what time was the flask shaken?

....

(1 mark)

(d) Sketch, on the graph on page 22, the curve that would have been obtained if a lump of the metal oxide had been used instead of powdered metal oxide.

(2 marks)

(e) By what other method could the rate at which oxygen is given off from the solution of hydrogen peroxide be altered?

....

(1 mark)

(f) Explain why the curve is horizontal between 270 and 330 seconds.

....

(1 mark)

Pyrogallol absorbs oxygen. When the gas in the syringe was shaken with sufficient pyrogallol to absorb all the oxygen present, 40 cm^3 of gas remained in the syringe.

(g) Name this gas, and state how it managed to get into the syringe.

....

....

(2 marks)

Turn over

(h) In this reaction bonds are broken and bonds are formed. The equation below shows the reaction taking place and the bonds that are broken and formed. The table gives the value of the strengths of the bonds.

$$H–O–O–H \rightarrow H–O–H + \tfrac{1}{2} O=O$$

Bond	Bond energy (kJ per mol)
H–O in hydrogen peroxide	487
H–O in water	463
O–O in hydrogen peroxide	146
O=O in oxygen	497

Work out the energy change for the decomposition of hydrogen peroxide, and say whether the reaction is exothermic or endothermic.

....

....

....

(3 marks)

Total: 16 marks

4. The diagram below shows how the atoms are arranged in monochloroethanamide.

(a) Give the name of each element present in monochloroethanamide and write down the arrangement of electrons of each atom. (The first one has been done for you.)

Name	Electronic structure
Nitrogen	2.5
....	....
....	....
....	....
....	....

(4 marks)

(b) Which of the above elements:

(i) is a halogen? ....

(ii) are used to manufacture ammonia? .... and ....

(iii) react together to give a colourless gas that fumes in moist air?

.... and ....

(iv) are obtained by fractional distillation of liquid?

.... and ....

(4 marks)

(c) Monochloroethanamide is a solid that melts at 129 °C and boils at 293 °C. State, with reasons, whether monochloroethanamide is a molecular or an ionic compound.

....

....

(2 marks)

Total: 10 marks

5. The boiling points of some of Group 1 metals are given below, together with their reactions with water.

Group I element	Boiling point °C	Reaction with water
lithium	180	fairly fast reaction, floats on water, but does not melt; hydrogen burns with a crimson flame
sodium	97.8	floats on water, metal melts; fast reaction, hydrogen burns with a yellow flame
potassium	63.7	floats on water, metal melts; very fast reaction, and explosive, hydrogen burns with a purple flame
rubidium		explosive reaction; hydrogen burns with a red flame

(a) What is the test for hydrogen gas?

....

....

(2 marks)

(b) Suggest which Group 1 metal would

   (i) not melt in boiling water?

....

   (ii) melt at room temperature (25 °C)?

....

(2 marks)

(c) Predict the reaction of caesium with water.

....

....

(2 marks)

Turn over

(d) Why are the Group 1 metals known as the alkali metals?

....

(1 mark)

(e) Suggest two reasons why Group 1 metals are kept under oil.

....

....

(2 marks)

(f) From the graph below, predict the boiling point of rubidium.

....

(1 mark)

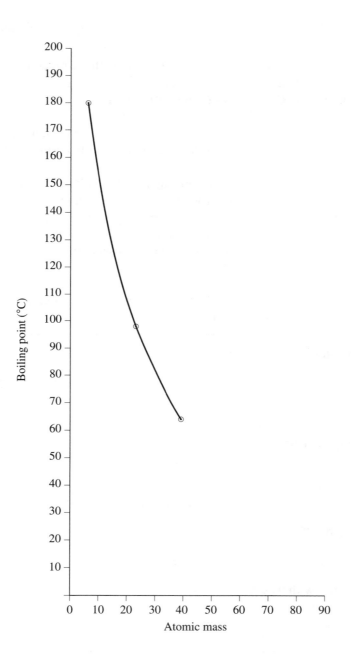

Total: 10 marks

6. A student tested 3 samples of water in order to compare their hardness. He used 50.0 cm³ samples of water and added soap solution, with shaking, 1.0 cm³ at a time until the lather formed lasted one minute. He then noted the appearance of the mixture at the end of each experiment.

Water sample	Volume of soap used to produce a lather (cm³)	Appearance of mixture after adding soap
Lake district – fairly soft		
London – very hard		
Soft water – rain water	1 cm³	no scum formed

(a) Name a chemical

(i) that causes temporary hardness in water

....

(ii) that causes permanent hardness in water

....

(2 marks)

(b) Complete (i) column 2 in the table above, choosing from the following figures:

5 cm³   12 cm³   50 cm³

(ii) column 3 above, to describe the appearance of the mixture at the end of the experiment.

(2 marks)

(c) What piece of equipment would the student use to measure *accurately*:

(i) 50.0 cm³ of water ....

(ii) 1.0 cm³ of soap solution ....

(2 marks)

(d) Name a chemical that removes *both* permanent hardness and temporary hardness from water.

....

(1 mark)

(e) Give **one** advantage and **one** disadvantage of living in a hard water area.

(i) advantage ....

(ii) disadvantage ....

(2 marks)

(f) Name the gas that dissolves in rain water to make it slightly acidic.

....

(1 mark)

Total: 10 marks

Turn over

7. Ethanol and carbon dioxide can be obtained from glucose ($C_6H_{12}O_6$) by a process known as fermentation. The reaction is catalysed by the *enzyme* zymase.

(a) (i) What is an *enzyme*?

....

....

(ii) Write the word equation for the preparation of ethanol from glucose.

....

(iii) Explain why an increase in temperature from body temperature to 100 °C slows down the rate of this reaction.

....

(4 marks)

(b) Ethanol can also be obtained from ethene.

(i) Write the word equation for this reaction.

....

(ii) Give one advantage and one disadvantage of making ethanol from ethene rather than by fermentation.

advantage ....

disadvantage ....

(3 marks)

(c) (i) Show that glucose and ethanoic acid have the same empirical formula.

....

....

(2 marks)

(ii) Describe a chemical test to distinguish between glucose and ethanoic acid.

....

....

(2 marks)

Total: 11 marks

8. The results below were obtained when separate 1.1 grams of powdered manganese were added to various volumes of 2.0 M hydrochloric acid. The volume of hydrogen was measured at room temperature and pressure.

Volume of 2.0 M HCl (cm^3)	Volume of hydrogen given off (cm^3)
5	120
10	240
15	360
20	480
25	480
30	480

(a) Plot a graph of volume of hydrogen given off (*y*-axis) against the volume of hydrochloric acid used (*x*-axis)

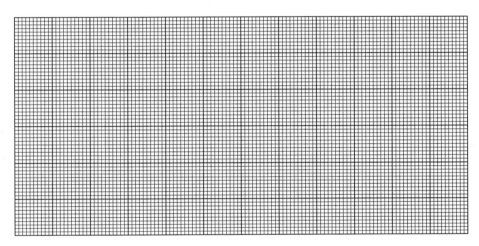

(4 marks)

(b) From your graph, find the volume of 2.0 M hydrochloric acid that is required to completely react with 1.1 g of manganese.

....

(1 mark)

(c) From your answer to (b) deduce:

(i) the volume of hydrochloric acid required to react with 1 mole of manganese

....

(ii) the number of moles of hydrochloric acid to react with 1 mole of manganese

....

(iii) the volume of hydrogen given off when 1 mole of manganese reacts with excess hydrochloric acid

....

Turn over

(iv) the number of moles of hydrogen given off when 1 mole of manganese reacts with excess hydrochloric acid

....

(v) The equation for the reaction between manganese and hydrochloric acid.

....

(5 marks)

Total: 10 marks

9. (a) Give two pieces of evidence which suggest that millions of years ago the Earth was made up of one land mass (Pangaea).

....

....

(2 marks)

It is thought that the earth's crust is broken up into about 12 tectonic plates which are slowly moving. New ocean crust is being formed continuously but the total area of these plates is believed to be constant.

(b) What causes the plates to move?

....

....

(2 marks)

(c) (i) Along the Californian coast, two continental plates meet. What is likely to happen when these plates slide past each other?

....

(1 mark)

(ii) Sometimes the tectonic plates move towards one another. Describe what happens when a thinner, denser oceanic plate collides with a thicker continental plate.

....

....

....

(3 marks)

Total: 8 marks

General Certificate of Secondary Education

Chemistry

Higher Paper 2

Time: 60 minutes

Instructions

■ Answer **all** the questions. Write your answers in the spaces provided.

■ Use a blue or black ink or ball-point pen.

■ Show all stages in any calculations and state the units.

Information for candidates

■ The number of marks is given in brackets at the end of each question or part-question. The total mark for the question is given at the end of the question.

■ Marks will **not** be deducted for wrong answers.

■ The Periodic Table is printed on page 52.

■ This paper has 5 questions. The maximum mark for this paper is 60.

Number	Mark
1.	
2.	
3.	
4.	
5.	

1. (a) Complete the following table by inserting the name or structural formula of the organic compound, then deciding whether it is a hydrocarbon and whether it is saturated or unsaturated. Some sections have already been completed for you.

Leave margin blank

Name	Structural formula	Hydrocarbon	Saturated/unsaturated
	H H $\mid$ $\mid$ H–C–C–H $\mid$ $\mid$ H H		
propene			unsaturated
	H H $\mid$ $\mid$ $-(C–C)_n$ $\mid$ $\mid$ H H		saturated
polyvinyl chloride	H H $\mid$ $\mid$ $-(C–C)_n$ $\mid$ $\mid$ H Cl	no	
ethanol	H H $\mid$ $\mid$ H–C–C–O–H $\mid$ $\mid$ H H		

(10 marks)

Turn over

(b) How would you show that propene was unsaturated?

....

....

(2 marks)

(c) Give the structural formula of the monomer from which the polymer, polyvinyl chloride, is made.

(2 marks)

Total: 14 marks

2. The graph below shows the current reading on an ammeter when dilute sulphuric acid was added to 50 cm^3 of aqueous barium hydroxide.

Volume of sulphuric acid added (cm^3)

When dilute sulphuric acid is added to aqueous barium hydroxide Ba(OH)$_2$ (an alkali) a white precipitate is formed.

(a) What is an alkali?

....

(1 mark)

(b) What is the chemical name of the white precipitate?

....

(1 mark)

(c) Construct the word equation and the chemical equation for this reaction.

word equation ....

(1 mark)

chemical equation ....

(2 marks)

(d) Explain the shape of the graph. You should include in your explanation the reason why the current drops to zero and why it increases again. You should also try to explain why the graph rises more rapidly than it falls.

....

....

....

....

(4 marks)

(e) What would be observed if a few drops of litmus solution were added to the aqueous barium hydroxide at the start of the experiment?

....

....

....

(3 marks)

(f) Suggest why, when hydrochloric acid of the same strength is used instead of sulphuric acid, the reading does not drop to zero and a change of direction in the current occurs at 10 cm^3.

....

....

(2 marks)

(g) Why is alternating current used in this experiment and not direct current?

....

(1 mark)

Total: 15 marks

3. Potassium chromate is soluble in water, forming a yellow solution. When silver nitrate is added to potassium chromate a red precipitate of silver chromate is formed.

(a) Name another compound that reacts with silver nitrate to form a coloured precipitate and give the colour of the precipitate

name of compound ....

colour of precipitate ....

(2 marks)

(b) An experiment was carried out in which various volumes of silver nitrate were added to the same volume of potassium chromate. The results are shown below.

0   1 cm³   2 cm³   3 cm³   4 cm³   5 cm³

→ volume of silver nitrate added

Turn over

(i) Identify the colours A, B and C in the diagrams on page 33.

A ....

B ....

C ....

(ii) Which one of the following ions is responsible for the colours obtained?

chromate   potassium   silver   nitrate

....

(4 marks)

(c) When the experiment was repeated with aluminium sulphate and sodium hydroxide, the following results were obtained.

(i) Name and give the formula of the white precipitate

....

....

(2 marks)

(ii) Explain the shape of the graph

....

....

(2 marks)

Total: 10 marks

4. Sulphuric acid can act as a dehydrating agent; a catalyst; an oxidising agent; a precipitating agent; and an acid. Explain, with reasons, how sulphuric acid is acting in each of the following reactions:

(i) $CuSO_4.5H_2O \rightarrow CuSO_4 + 5H_2O$

....

because ....

(ii) $H_2SO_4 + Na_2CO_3 \rightarrow Na_2SO_4 + H_2O + CO_2$

....

because ....

(iii) $C_2H_5OH \rightarrow C_2H_4 + H_2O$

....

because ....

(iv) $Ba(NO_3)_2 + H_2SO_4 \rightarrow BaSO_4 + 2HNO_3$

....

because ....

(v) $Cu + 2H_2SO_4 \rightarrow CuSO_4 + 2H_2O + SO_2$

....

because ....

(vi) $CH_3CO_2H + C_2H_5OH \rightarrow CH_3CO_2C_2H_5 + H_2O$

....

because ....

(12 marks)

Total: 12 marks

5. Consider the reversible reaction for the formation of ozone from oxygen

$$3O_2 \text{ (g)} \rightleftharpoons 2O_3 \text{ (g)}$$

The formation of ozone is endothermic.

Ozone is a pale blue, poisonous gas.

(a) (i) Name, and (ii) give the formula of, another coloured, poisonous gas.

(i) .... (ii) ....

(2 marks)

(b) The reaction achieves dynamic equilibrium when 10% of ozone is present.

(i) Explain what is meant by 'dynamic equilibrium'.

....

....

(2 marks)

Turn over

(ii) Suggest, with a reason, one method of increasing the yield of ozone.

....

....

(2 marks)

(c) Ozone is a much more powerful oxidising agent than oxygen. It will oxidise lead(II) sulphide to form lead(II) sulphate and oxygen only. Construct the equation for this reaction.

....

(3 marks)

Total: 9 marks

Solutions to practice exam papers

Each * represents 1 mark. Make sure your answer is correct before you award yourself the mark – if you are not sure ask your teacher or another responsible person. Text written in brackets is NOT required to score the mark.

The tip at the end of each question will help you with your revision.

Solutions to Foundation 1

1.

Compound	Soluble	Insoluble
sodium carbonate	✓	
aluminium nitrate	✓ *	
barium chloride	✓ *	
zinc sulphate	✓ *	
lead carbonate		✓ *

One mark for each correctly placed tick   **Total: 4 marks**

> **TIP**
> **All** Group I metal compounds are soluble; **all** nitrates are soluble and **all** chlorides are soluble **except** silver chloride and lead chloride.

2. (a) 18 protons *; 18 electrons *; 22 neutrons *   **3 marks**

   (b) (i) potassium * (ii) Group 1 * (iii) calcium * (iv) Group 2 *   **4 marks**

   (c) (i) magnesium * (ii) hydrogen * (iii) magnesium oxide *   **3 marks**

   (d) (i) nitrogen * (ii) 80% *   **2 marks**

   (e) in light bulbs or where a non-reactive atmosphere is required *   **1 mark**

   (f) (i) does not burn * (ii) too dense, balloon will not float *   **2 marks**   **Total: 15 marks**

> **TIP**
> You should have used your Periodic Table to answer this question. In a neutral atom the number of protons equals the number of electrons. The mass number is the number of protons PLUS the number of neutrons. When the question asks for a name, it is a mistake to give a symbol or formula.
>   For the noble gas group the physical properties increase going down the group; thus melting point, boiling point and density all increase from helium to radon.

3. (a) oxygen * (b) increases * (c) 20% *   **3 marks**

   (d) the volume of gas left would have been greater *; some of the oxygen is used up in breathing and produces carbon dioxide * (which does not react with iron)   **2 marks**

   (e) nitrogen or argon, or some other unreactive gas*   **1 mark**

(f) ammonia is very soluble in water *, hence when the apparatus is heated more ammonia will be produced and give wrong results *   **2 marks**

(g) that ammonia is made up of nitrogen and hydrogen only *   **1 mark**

(h) as a catalyst *   **1 mark**

(i) yes, because one of the products is hydrogen * and hydrogen burns in air *   **2 marks**

Total: 12 marks

> **TIP**
>
> In these experiments iron is behaving in two ways: (i) it reacts with the oxygen in the air for the first experiment; and (ii) it acts as a catalyst for the decomposition of ammonia into nitrogen and hydrogen. The actual volume in this second experiment doubles, i.e. 40 cm^3 of ammonia gives 20 cm^3 of nitrogen and 60 cm^3 of hydrogen. Ammonia does burn in pure oxygen, but it does not burn in air.

4. (a) more reactive *; reactivity of metals increases down the group *   **2 marks**

(b) (i) under oil * (ii) it is a reactive metal and reacts with oxygen in the air at room temperature*

2 marks

(c) white precipitate (of barium carbonate) *; solution goes clear (as soluble barium hydrogencarbonate is formed) *   **2 marks**

(d) both acids react with insoluble barium carbonate * to form soluble salts (barium chloride or barium nitrate) *   **2 marks**   **Total: 8 marks**

> **TIP**
>
> Chemical reactivity increases down the group for Group 1 and Group 2, thus barium is much more reactive than magnesium. Reactive metals such as sodium, potassium, calcium and barium are kept under oil because they react rapidly with oxygen, and they do not react with oil and are denser than oil.
>
> Elements in the same group have similar properties. However, barium sulphate is one of the insoluble salts of barium: barium chloride or barium nitrate is used as a test for the sulphate ion; if a sulphate ion is present, a white precipitate is formed.

5. (a) (i) Group 3 period 3 * (ii) transition metal period 4 *   **2 marks**

(b) any two from: forms coloured compounds *; shows variable valency *; high melting points, or high boiling points, or high density *   **2 marks**

(c) aluminium has a (protective) oxide layer of aluminium oxide (which has to be removed)*; *either* this has to be removed before acid starts to react, *or* the oxide layer of iron reacts readily with acids *   **2 marks**

(d)

	aluminium oxide	iron(III) oxide
formula of oxide	**Al_2O_3** *	Fe_2O_3
name of ore containing oxide	**bauxite** *	haematite
method of extracting metal from its ore	electrolysis	**reduction with carbon** *
use of metal	manufacture of pots and pans	**manufacture of steel** *
reaction of oxide with dilute hydrochloric acid	reacts to give a colourless solution	**reacts to give a green solution** *
reaction with sodium hydroxide	**reacts to give a colourless solution** *	no reaction
use as a catalyst	converting ethanol to ethene	**manufacture of ammonia from nitrogen and hydrogen** *

7 marks

(e) ore is a rock from which a metal * can be economically extracted *   **2 marks**

(f) (i) iron is cheaper than aluminium * (ii) aluminium is less dense than iron *   **2 marks**

(g) heat the rust (gently) *; condense the liquid given off *; show that it boils at 100 °C *   **3 marks**

Total: 20 marks

> **TIP**
>
> Learn the properties of transition metals – note that high melting point and high boiling point is considered as one property. Because aluminium is a reactive metal it is made by electrolysis. Note also that iron forms a basic oxide but aluminium forms an amphoteric oxide (reacts with both acids and alkalis). Some car bodies are made of aluminium alloys, but they are very expensive. Rusting of iron is unusual because the hydrated iron oxide formed flakes from the surface of iron and does not remain attached to the iron.

6. (a) carbon dioxide *   **1 mark**

(b) size of crystals * either small rounded grains (sandstone) or pale large crystals (granite) *

2 marks

(c)

igneous	metamorphic	sedimentary
granite	marble	sandstone
	slate	limestone

One mark for each column correct   **3 marks**

(d) high temperatures * and high pressures * (required to build mountain ranges)   **2 marks**

(e) (i) shapes fit *; fossils found in South America are also found in Africa *

(ii) continental drift *   **3 marks**   **Total: 11 marks**

TIP

A key is a very useful way to classify anything, including animals and chemicals. Learn about the rock cycle and how to distinguish between igneous, metamorphic and sedimentary rock.

7. (a) (i) noble gases had not been discovered * (ii) electricity had not been discovered (therefore there was no way of obtaining aluminium from alumina) * **2 marks**

   (b) (i) F * (ii) D * and E * (iii) A, B *, C and F * (iv) E * (v) C * **7 marks**

   (c) NH_3 * **1 mark**

   (d) (i) C_2H_4 * (ii) CH_2* **2 marks**

   (e) (i) (pungent) smell * (ii) turns blue * **2 marks** **Total: 14 marks**

TIP

Although this question uses symbols devised by Dalton, you can easily use modern-day symbols. Dalton had not included the noble gases because they had not been discovered when he wrote his atomic theory (helium was discovered in 1868). Aluminium was not extracted from alumina using electricity until 1886.

   Diatomic means two atoms per molecule. Most non-metallic elements (except the noble gases) are diatomic – noble gases are monatomic – one atom per molecule.

8. (a) (i) magnesium, because it displaces copper from copper(II) oxide * **1 mark**

   (ii) gives out heat * **1 mark**

   (iii) copper + magnesium oxide * **1 mark**

   (iv) magnesium *, copper and magnesium oxide * **2 marks**

   (b) copper is a **copper coloured/ brown/red** * metal

   magnesium is a silvery shiny **metal** *

   magnesium oxide is a **white** * solid **3 marks**

   (c) (i) add excess * sulphuric acid *; filter *; wash residue with distilled water*; dry in an oven *

   5 marks

   (Marks can be scored from diagrams)

   (ii) copper conducts electricity * **1 mark**

   (d) making electric wires *; making pans, or water heaters, or water pipes *; making brass * (any two uses) **2 marks** **Total: 16 marks**

TIP

More reactive metals displace less reactive metals from their compounds. Notice that in (a) (iv) it tells you that EXCESS magnesium was used, therefore some will be left over at the end of the experiment.

   Sulphuric acid reacts with both magnesium and magnesium oxide to form soluble magnesium sulphate but does not react with copper. The copper must be washed to remove other impurities such as magnesium sulphate – it must be heated gently otherwise it will be oxidised to copper(II) oxide.

   The only reliable test for any metal is that it conducts electricity.

Solutions to Foundation 2

1. (a) endothermic *   **1 mark**

    (b) A solution that has dissolved as much of the solute as possible * at a particular temperature *

    2 marks

    (c) point correctly plotted *; smooth curve drawn *; line crosses *y*-axis *   **3 marks**

    (d) between 16 and 18 grams (per 100 grams of water)*   **1 mark**

    (e) (i) 74 * – 18 = 56 grams * (answer will depend on the graph but should be in the region of 54 to 60 grams)

    (ii) crystals will be much larger *   **3 marks**

    (f) excessive plant growth in rivers or lakes *, leading to a reduction in dissolved oxygen in the water * (causing animal and plant life to die)   **2 marks**   **Total: 12 marks**

> **TIP**
> The solubility of a salt normally increases with increase in temperature. Potassium nitrate is a very soluble salt. Cooling slowly produces larger crystals – the same effect occurs when molten rock cools slowly.

2. (a) (i) 25 seconds * (ii) 13 seconds *   **2 marks**

    (b) (i) 10 seconds * (ii) 3 seconds *   **2 marks**

    (The above results will depend upon the accuracy of your reading of the graph)

    (c) (i) no effect *; no effect *

    (iv) slower *; no effect *   **4 marks**

    (d) heat the water *   **1 mark**   **Total: 9 marks**

> **TIP**
> The maximum amount of hydrogen formed is 240 cm^3, so half the calcium will have reacted when 120 cm^3 of hydrogen is given off. Note that calcium reacts more slowly with water than with hydrochloric acid – fewer hydrogen ions in the water.
> Since the water is in excess, then adding more water to the water already present will have no effect. Adding water to the hydrochloric acid will slow down the reaction (it is more dilute), but will not affect the final volume of hydrogen.
> The rates of reaction can be increased by (i) increasing the temperature; (ii) increasing the concentration; and (iii) adding a catalyst. In this reaction it is impossible to increase the concentration of water and there is no suitable catalyst.

3. (a) filtration or sieving *   **1 mark**

    (b) (i) turns damp litmus paper red *, then bleaches the litmus paper *

    (ii) chlorine sterilises the water * (kills bacteria)   **3 marks**

    (c) temporary hardness can be removed by boiling *; permanent hardness cannot be removed by boiling *   **2 marks**

    (d) (i) calcium sulphate or magnesium sulphate *

    (ii) calcium hydrogencarbonate or magnesium hydrogencarbonate *

    (iii) sodium carbonate *   **3 marks**

(e) (i) both calcium sulphate and magnesium sulphate are soluble in water *

(ii) rain water (which is carbon dioxide dissolved in water) reacts with calcium/magnesium carbonate * to form soluble calcium/magnesium hydrogencarbonate *   **3 marks**

Total: 12 marks

> **TIP**
>
> Filtration is used to remove an insoluble solid from water. Note that chlorine turns damp litmus paper red before bleaching it. All sodium salts are soluble, so by adding sodium carbonate it precipitates the insoluble calcium carbonate and magnesium carbonate. Remember that rain is a weak solution of carbonic acid (carbon dioxide dissolved in water) – rain water might contain other pollutants such as sulphur dioxide and oxides of nitrogen.

4. (a) (i) calcium carbonate * (ii) calcium oxide *   **2 marks**

(b) (i) carbon dioxide from the thermal decomposition of limestone *

(ii) carbon monoxide from the incomplete combustion * of methane/natural gas fuel *

(iii) nitrogen from the air *   **4 marks**

(c) (i) either (as a flux) for the extraction of iron, or for foundations for roads, or making cement, or making glass *

(ii) either in agriculture to neutralise acidity in the soil, or steel-making, or a constituent in mortar, or for purifying water, or making calcium hydroxide *

(iii) fire extinguishers, or in fizzy drinks *   **3 marks**   **Total: 9 marks**

> **TIP**
>
> Whenever air is used in an industrial process, the nitrogen is not used up. Nitrogen is present, for example, in the waste gases from the manufacture of iron. Note that incomplete combustion of a hydrocarbon (in this case methane), produces the poisonous gas carbon monoxide.

5. (a) a hydrocarbon *   **1 mark**

(b) carbon *; hydrogen *   **2 marks**

(c) fractional distillation *   **1 mark**

(d) (i) a solution in water *   **1 mark**

(ii) either it is strongly acidic, or it contains a high concentration of hydrogen ions *   **1 mark**

(e) either coal, or peat, or any solid fossil fuel, or something made from wood such as newspapers or rags *   **1 mark**

(f) either charcoal or carbon *   **1 mark**

(g) 'sucking back' might occur, or description of sucking back such as vapours would condense causing a vacuum * and water would be sucked in to fill the vacuum causing the hot glass to crack *   **2 marks**   **Total: 10 marks**

> **TIP**
>
> If a compound burns to form carbon dioxide and water it must contain carbon and hydrogen – the oxygen will have come from the air. Acids have a pH below 7. You were expected to work out that a substance similar to wood would produce a similar reaction.

6. (a) sodium (most reactive); iron; gold (least reactive)

three correct – 2 marks; two correct – 1 mark   **2 marks**

(b) (i) iron nail * (ii) either 'drying agent', or named drying agent such as anhydrous calcium chloride *   (iii) either air-free or boiled water * (iv) either ordinary water or water plus air *   **4 marks**

(c) (i) either gold is less common than sodium in the Earth's crust, or gold ores are not as rich as sodium ores*

(ii) sodium extraction uses electricity, which is a more expensive process than using coke in the manufacture of iron *   **2 marks**   **Total: 8 marks**

> **TIP**
> Any metal that occurs in the free state must be very unreactive. Thus silver and gold are low in the reactivity series. Both water AND air are necessary for iron to rust. The presence of a salt, such as sodium chloride, speeds up rusting. That is why cars rust more quickly in coastal regions.

Solutions to Higher I

1. (a) sublimation *   **1 mark**

(b)

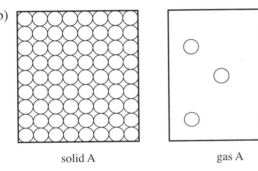

solid A   gas A   * *   **2 marks**

(c)

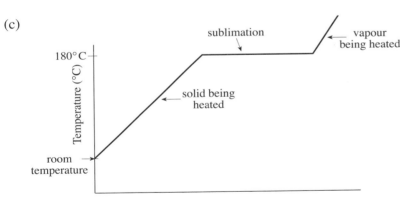

starts at room temperature *
horizontal section at 180 ° *
correct shape *

3 marks

(d) temperature above 100 °C required *   **1 mark**

(e) (i) iodine * (ii) low sublimation temperature * (iii) either carbon, or sulphur, or phosphorus *

3 marks

Total: 10 marks

> **TIP**
> There are a few solid non-metals; they include iodine, carbon, sulphur and phosphorus. Note the arrangement of particles in solids, liquids and gases – in solids there is an orderly arrangement of particles. The arrangements get more random moving from liquids to gases and the particles in a gas are much further apart than in a liquid.

2. (a) X is hydrochloric acid (or nitric acid) * NOT sulphuric acid; Y is calcium carbonate (marble chips) or any other metallic carbonate *   **2 marks**

   (b) it is denser than air *   **1 mark**

   (c) (i) either a liquid hydrocarbon such as petrol or an alcohol such as ethanol *

      (ii) carbon * (iii) carbon monoxide * (iv) either copper(II) carbonate or any carbonate of a metal low in the reactivity series * (vi) either sugar or a carbohydrate *   **5 marks**

   (d) :O×C×O: * *   (1 mark for correct number of electrons on each atom – and one mark for sharing 2 pairs of electrons)   **2 marks**

   (e) carbon dioxide is made of simple molecules *; silicon dioxide has a giant molecular structure *

      2 marks

   (f) iron *   **1 mark**

   (g) 3 moles of gas formed * therefore volume is $3 \times 24 = 72$ litres *   **2 marks**   **Total: 15 marks**

TIP

Sulphuric acid cannot be used because it forms a layer of insoluble calcium sulphate. You can only use properties that can be identified from the diagram, thus although carbon dioxide does not support burning, this cannot be deduced from the diagram.

Note that the wording for (c) indicates that there can be more than one possible answer.

Since carbon dioxide is made up of discrete molecules it is a gas; silicon dioxide, on the other hand, has a giant structure and is therefore a solid.

Note in (g) 2 moles of ammonia gas are formed as well as 1 mole of carbon dioxide. The question asked the **total** volume of gas given off, not just carbon dioxide.

---

3. (a) relights * a glowing splint *   **2 marks**

   (b) (i) either manganese(IV) oxide or copper(II) oxide *

      (ii) transition metal *

      (iii) either coloured compounds, or variable valency, or high density, or high melting (boiling) points *

      (iv) either iron in the Haber process, or platinum in the contact process, or any other suitable catalyst with a named industrial process *   **4 marks**

   (c) 81 seconds *   **1 mark**

   (d) slower rate of reaction * same volume of oxygen *   **2 marks**

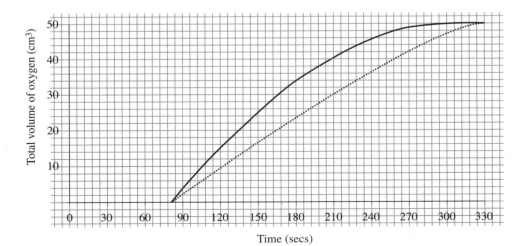

(e) either by changing the temperature, or by changing the concentration of the hydrogen peroxide *

1 mark

(f) the reaction had finished *   **1 mark**

(g) nitrogen *; from the air in the apparatus *   **2 marks**

(h) Energy required to break bonds = $2 \times 487 + 146 = 1120$ *

Energy given out when bonds are formed = $2 \times 463 + \frac{1}{2} \times 497 = 1174.5$ *

Energy change is $+1120 - 1174.5 = -54.5$ kJ, so it is exothermic *   **3 marks**   **Total: 16 marks**

TIP

The metal oxide catalyst has to be black. The time at which the flask is shaken can be found from the point on the graph when the rate begins to increase rapidly (an answer $+$ or $-$ 3 of 81 seconds is acceptable).

Lumps of catalyst act more slowly than a powdered catalyst because there is less area for contact.

Once all the reaction has finished no more oxygen is given off.

The energy change in a chemical reaction is the difference between the energy required to break bonds (endothermic) and the energy given out when bonds are formed (exothermic).

---

4. (a) Hydrogen 1 *

Carbon 2.4 *

Oxygen 2.6 *

Chlorine 2.8.7 *   **4 marks**

(b) (i) Cl * (ii) N and H * (iii) H and Cl * (iv) N and O *   **4 marks**

(c) molecular *; it has a low melting (boiling) point *   **2 marks**   **Total: 10 marks**

TIP

The arrangements can be worked out from the Periodic Table – thus carbon is in period 2, Group 4 (2,4) and chlorine in period 3 and Group 7 (2,8,7).

Hydrogen chloride fumes in moist air and nitrogen and oxygen are made by fractional distillation of liquid air.

Most organic compounds are molecular.

---

5. (a) burns * with a 'pop' *   **2 marks**

(b) (i) Li * (ii) Cs or Fr *   **2 marks**

(c) react explosively *; hydrogen burns with a coloured flame *   **2 marks**

(d) because their oxides and hydroxides are alkalis *   **1 mark**

(e) they react with air *; either they are denser than oil, or they do not react with oil*   **2 marks**

(f) around 40 °C   **1 mark**

Total: 10 marks

TIP

The melting points and boiling points of Group I metals decrease down the group, but they get more reactive. From your Periodic Table, the atomic mass of Rb is 85 and hence you should extrapolate your curve to obtain the boiling point. Cs melts at 29 °C.

Caesium gives a blue colour to the hydrogen flame.

Oxides and hydroxides of Group I metals are alkalis – they dissolve in water to give solutions with a pH greater than 7.

6. (a) (i) calcium (magnesium) hydrogen carbonate * (ii) calcium (magnesium) sulphate *   **2 marks**

(b)

Water sample	Volume of soap used to produce a lather (cm³)	Appearance of mixture after adding soap
Lake district – fairly soft	**5 cm³**	**some scum formed ***
London – very hard	**12 cm³**	**a lot of scum formed ***
Soft water – rain water	1 cm³	no scum formed

(one mark for each correct line)   **2 marks**

(c) (i) either a pipette or burette * (ii) burette *   **2 marks**

(d) sodium carbonate *   **1 mark**

(e) (i) either healthier to drink, or gives water a pleasant taste, or provides calcium for developing strong teeth and bones * (ii) either produces kettle fur or boiler scale, or forms a great deal of scum with soap *   **2 marks**

(f) carbon dioxide *   **1 mark**   **Total: 10 marks**

TIP

Hard water adds to the cost of living since more soap is required and the deposition of fur and scale means more energy is required to heat water.

A burette or pipette must be used to measure accurately the volume of water – a measuring cylinder is far too inaccurate.

The question asked for the gas that makes the water **slightly** acidic – pollutants such as sulphur dioxide and oxides of nitrogen make the water **very** acidic.

7. (a) (i) biological * catalyst *

(ii) glucose + water → ethanol + carbon dioxide *

(iii) the enzyme is denatured at temperatures over body temperature *   **4 marks**

(b) (i) ethene + water → ethanol *   **1 mark**

(ii) advantage – either fast, or pure ethanol, or continuous *

disadvantage – uses up non-renewable resources *   **2 marks**

(c) (i) glucose ($C_6H_{12}O_6$) has the empirical formula CH_2O; ethanoic acid is CH_3CO_2H *, which can be written as $C_2H_4O_2$ so it also has the empirical formula CH_2O *

(In essence, one mark for CH_3CO_2H and one mark for CH_2O)   **2 marks**

(ii) Add a suitable indicator *; colour change would show acid present *

e.g. add pH paper *; solution turns orange for ethanoic acid, no change for glucose solution *
or add a carbonate * fizz only with acids * or with Fehlings * red precipitate only with glucose *

2 marks

Total: 11 marks

TIP

Enzymes are denatured at about 40 °C, and by acidity.
    There are two main methods of making ethanol – one by fermentation (a batch process) and the other from ethene (a continuous process).
    Always try to think of a simple test to distinguish between substances – in this case acidity is the obvious answer rather than trying to prove that glucose is present.

---

8. (a) points correctly plotted *; axes suitably labelled *; suitable scale chosen *; curve drawn *

    4 marks

    (b) 20 cm^3 *   **1 mark**

    (c) (i) 20 cm^3 of acid reacted with 1.1 g of manganese

        $20 \times 50 = 1000$ cm^3 * (of HCl reacts with 1 mole – 55 grams of manganese)

    (ii) 2 moles *

    (iii) $480 \times 50 = 24\,000$ cm^3 *

    (iv) 1 mole *

    (v) $Mn + 2HCl \rightarrow H_2 + MnCl_2$ *   **5 marks**   **Total: 10 marks**

TIP

The graph will be a straight line passing through the origin (if there is no acid, then no gas will be given off). A solution containing 2.0 M hydrochloric acid contains 2 moles of the acid in 1 litre (1000 cm^3) of solvent. One mole of gas at room temperature and pressure occupies 24 000 cm^3.

---

9. (a) shape of present-day continents; similar fossils are found in parts of the world very far apart; magnetic records * * (any two points)   **2 marks**

    (b) (Continental drift which is explained by) plate tectonics *; plates move, possibly driven by convection currents *   **2 marks**

    (c) (i) a mountain range is formed * (ii) the less dense plate is forced down (subduction) *, heat is produced (which melts surrounding rock) *, causing volcanic activity *   **4 marks**

    Total: 8 marks

TIP

The idea of one land mass, the Pangaea, is better seen if one uses the continental shelf boundaries rather than the coastal boundaries. It is now assumed that the Earth is made up of six large and several smaller plates in a constant state of motion. The direction of movement can be deduced from volcanic and earthquake activites.

Solutions to Higher 2

1. (a)

Name	Structural formula	Hydrocarbon	Saturated/unsaturated
ethane *	H H | | H–C–C–H | | H H	yes *	yes *
propene	H H H \\ | / C=C–C–H * / \\ H H	yes *	unsaturated
poly(ethene) *	H H | | $+$C–C$\!\!+_n$ | | H H	yes *	saturated
polyvinyl chloride	H H | | $+$C–C$\!\!+_n$ | | H Cl	no	saturated *
ethanol	H H | | H–C–C–O–H | | H H	no *	saturated *

10 marks

(b) Add bromine water *; solution goes from brown to colourless (or is decolourised) *   **2 marks**

(c) double bond between carbon atoms *; correct formula *   **2 marks**   **Total: 14 marks**

TIP

Unsaturated compounds contain multiple bonds (double or triple) between carbon atoms. Polymers are made from monomers containing double bonds.

---

2. (a) a soluble base *   **1 mark**

(b) barium sulphate *   **1 mark**

(c) sulphuric acid + barium hydroxide $\rightarrow$ barium sulphate + water *   **1 mark**

$$H_2SO_4 + Ba(OH)_2 \rightarrow BaSO_4 + 2H_2O **$$

(One mark for correct left-hand side; one mark for correct right-hand side)   **2 marks**

(d) Current drops because Ba^{2+} and SO_4^{2-} are removed as precipitate *; water is formed which is a non-conductor *; after 5 cm^3 no ions are left in solution *; sulphuric acid conducts electricity better than barium hydroxide *   **4 marks**

(e) blue at start (excess barium hydroxide) *; purple/mauve after 5 cm^3 *; then finally red (excess sulphuric acid) *   **3 marks**

(f) barium chloride is soluble in water, so the only ions removed are those that form water (H^+ and OH^-) *; sulphuric acid is dibasic, i.e. contains two replaceable H^+ ions, whereas hydrochloric acid is monobasic *   **2 marks**

(g) direct current would cause electrolysis to occur (thus changing the concentrations of the solutions) *   **1 mark**   **Total: 15 marks**

Titrations can also be carried out using the method described here, i.e. conduction experiments. If we write the equation as ions we get:

$$Ba^{2+}(aq) + 2OH^-(aq) + 2H^+(aq) + SO_4^{2-}(aq) \rightarrow BaSO_4(s) + 2H_2O(l)$$

As you can see, there are ions on the left-hand side so the solution conducts, but none on the right-hand side. As the reaction proceeds, the current falls until the reaction is complete (at 5 cm^3); it then rises as more sulphuric acid is added.

If we write the ionic equation for hydrochloric acid we get:

$$Ba^{2+}(aq) + 2OH^-(aq) + 2H^+(aq) + 2Cl^-(aq) \rightarrow Ba^{2+}(aq) + 2Cl^-(aq) + 2H_2O(l)$$

Here you will see that there are also ions on the right-hand side, so the mixture still conducts electricity. Also, you see in this equation that 1 mole of barium hydroxide reacts with 2 moles of hydrochloric acid whereas with sulphuric acid they react one mole to one mole.

3. (a) silver iodide *; yellow * (there are others you may have chosen)   **2 marks**

    (b) (i) A is red *; B is colourless *; C is yellow * (ii) chromate *   **4 marks**

    (c) (i) aluminium hydroxide *; $Al(OH)_3$ *   **2 marks**

       (ii) aluminium hydroxide is amphoteric *, therefore it 'dissolves' in excess sodium hydroxide solution *   **2 marks**   **Total: 10 marks**

One of the properties of transition metals is that they form coloured salts. Chromate (CrO_4^{2-}) contains the transition metal chromium.

Aluminium hydroxide is amphoteric; it reacts with both acids and alkalis. It reacts with sodium hydroxide to form the soluble salt sodium aluminate.

4. (i) dehydrating agent *; water removed from hydrated copper(II) sulphate *

    (ii) acid *; acid reacts with carbonates to form (a salt plus water plus) carbon dioxide *

    (iii) dehydrating agent *; (elements of) water removed from ethanol *

    (iv) precipitating reagent *; forms insoluble barium sulphate *

    (v) oxidising agent *; copper oxidised to copper (II) salt *

    (vi) catalyst *; it does not take part in the reaction *   **12 marks**   **Total: 12 marks**

You were given a clue at the start of this question. Make sure you understand the properties of acids, dehydrating agents and oxidising agents, and what is meant by a precipitation reaction. Copper is oxidised because its oxidation number has increased from 0 to +2. In reaction (i) you would see a colour change of blue to white. Note that in the last reaction sulphuric acid is not one of the reactants – it catalyses the reaction – you were meant to deduce this.

5. (a) (i) chlorine * (ii) Cl_2 *   **2 marks**

   (b) (i) The rate of the forward reaction * equals the rate of the reverse reaction *   **2 marks**

   (ii) Since 3 volumes are going to two volumes *, increasing the pressure would produce more ozone * *or* since the reaction is endothermic *, increase the temperature *   **2 marks**

   (c) $PbS + 2O_3 \rightarrow PbSO_4 + O_2$

   formula of left-hand side correct *; formula of right-hand side correct *; correctly balanced *

   3 marks

   Total: 9 marks

TIP

Another gas that is poisonous and coloured is the brown gas nitrogen dioxide. Applying Le Chatelier's principle, increasing pressure and increasing temperature will increase the yield of ozone (however, ozone is unstable to heat and would probably break down to oxygen).

When you balance the equation, note that the formulae must be correct and that there must be the same number of atoms on each side of the equation.

How well did you do?

Here is a guide to the grades you might obtain, after adding together the marks you obtained for the Foundation and Higher papers. The maximum mark is 160.

Foundation		Higher	
Mark	**Grade**	**Mark**	**Grade**
>128	C	>140	A*
112–127	D	128–139	A
96–111	E	112–127	B
80–95	F	96–111	C
64–79	G	80–95	D
<64	U	<80	U

If you do not reach grade G on the Foundation Tier papers you will be unclassified (U) and the result will not appear on your GCSE certificate. If you fail to reach grade D on the Higher Tier papers you will be unclassified (U) and the result will not appear on your GCSE certificate.

This is why it is important that you enter at the right level.

Periodic Table

1	2											3	4	5	6	7	0
							1 H Hydrogen										4 He Helium 2
7 Li Lithium 3	9 Be Beryllium 4											11 B Boron 5	12 C Carbon 6	14 N Nitrogen 7	16 O Oxygen 8	19 F Fluorine 9	20 Ne Neon 10
23 Na Sodium 11	24 Mg Magnesium 12											27 Al Aluminium 13	28 Si Silicon 14	31 P Phosphorus 15	32 S Sulphur 16	35.5 Cl Chlorine 17	40 Ar Argon 18
39 K Potassium 19	40 Ca Calcium 20	45 Sc Scandium 21	48 Ti Titanium 22	51 V Vanadium 23	52 Cr Chromium 24	55 Mn Manganese 25	56 Fe Iron 26	59 Co Cobalt 27	59 Ni Nickel 28	63.5 Cu Copper 29	65 Zn Zinc 30	70 Ga Gallium 31	73 Ge Germanium 32	75 As Arsenic 33	79 Se Selenium 34	80 Br Bromine 35	84 Kr Krypton 36
85 Rb Rubidium 37	88 Sr Strontium 38	89 Y Yttrium 39	91 Zr Zirconium 40	93 Nb Niobium 41	96 Mo Molybdenum 42	Tc Technetium 43	101 Ru Ruthenium 44	103 Rh Rhodium 45	106 Pd Palladium 46	108 Ag Silver 47	112 Cd Cadmium 48	115 In Indium 49	119 Sn Tin 50	122 Sb Antimony 51	128 Te Tellurium 52	127 I Iodine 53	131 Xe Xenon 54
133 Cs Caesium 55	137 Ba Barium 56	139 La Lanthanum 57	178 Hf Hafnium 72	181 Ta Tantalum 73	184 W Tungsten 74	186 Re Rhenium 75	190 Os Osmium 76	192 Ir Iridium 77	195 Pt Platinum 78	197 Au Gold 79	201 Hg Mercury 80	204 Tl Thallium 81	207 Pb Lead 82	209 Bi Bismuth 83	Po Polonium 84	At Astatine 85	222 Rn Radon 86
Fr Francium 87	226 Ra Radium 88	227 Ac Actinium 89															

Lanthanum series (58–71)

140 Ce Cerium 58	141 Pr Praseodymium 59	144 Nd Neodymium 60	Pm Promethium 61	150 Sm Samarium 62	152 Eu Europium 63	157 Gd Gadolinium 64	159 Tb Terbium 65	162 Dy Dysprosium 66	165 Ho Holmium 67	167 Er Erbium 68	169 Tm Thulium 69	173 Yb Ytterbium 70	175 Lu Lutetium 71

Actinium series (90–103)

232 Th Thorium 90	231 Pa Protactinium 91	238 U Uranium 92	Np Neptunium 93	Pu Plutonium 94	Am Americium 95	Cm Curium 96	Bk Berkelium 97	Cf Californium 98	Es Einsteinium 99	Fm Fermium 100	Md Mendelevium 101	No Nobelium 102	Lr Lowrencium 103

∗58 – 57 Lanthanum series
†90 – 103 Actinium series

Elements for which no relative atomic mass is shown are not naturally occurring.